<u>Table of Contents</u>

1

INTRODUCTION

As a quiz enthusiast who has engaged in quizzing for over 25 years, I'm willing to share my knowledge with your all. 300 questions are covering Geography,History and Politics and General Knowledge each quiz questions and answers are provided in this book. Questions have been designed to enable quiz lovers to test and improve their knowledge.

To be a good Quizzer you have to constantly search and update your knowledge. Based on these questions and answers you may search more and gather more knowledge. Join me to navigate you through the universe of knowledge.

Quiz 01: Countries of the World

Questions

1) What is the smallest country within mainland Africa which is surrounded by Senegal, except for its western coast on the Atlantic Ocean?

2) Which country is landlocked within South Africa?

3) Previously known as French Somaliland, It was a country located in the Horn of Africa. It is bordered by Eritrea in the north, Ethiopia in the west and south, and Somalia in the southeast. The remainder of the border is formed by the Red Sea and the Gulf of Aden at the east. It is known by a different name Since its independence in 1967. What is this country?

4) A doubly landlocked country is surrounded by landlocked countries. There are only two doubly landlocked countries in the world. One is Liechtenstein, What is the other country?

5) Brazil borders every country in South America except two. What are they?

6) The largest landlocked country in the world is in Central Asia, covering a total area of 2,724,900 square km and has a population of 16.3 million people. What is this country?

7) Located in Southeast Asia, it is a small country of 15,410 square km. It became the first new sovereign state of the 21st century in 2002. It is one of only two predominantly Roman Catholic countries in Asia. as well as the only country of Asia to be located completely in the Southern Hemisphere. What is this country?

8) The Commonwealth of Nations has only two out of its 54 member states that do not have any past constitutional link to the British Empire or another Commonwealth member The first such country was Mozambique. What is the other country which was a Belgian trust territory that had been a German colony until World War I, admitted to Commonwealth membership in 2009?

9) It is a landlocked country in Asia which borders Russia and China. It covers an area of 1,564,116 square kilometers, with a population of just 3.3 million, making it the world's most sparsely populated independent country in the world with an average population of 2 people per sq/km. Name this country?

10) In terms of comparing its length to its width,
Which Latin American country is regarded as
the narrowest country in the world?

Quiz 02: Rivers

Questions

1) Flowing through Central Russia to Southern Russia and into the Caspian Sea, it has a length of 3,531 km making it the longest river in Europe. What is this river?

2) The 4th longest in Africa, this is the largest river flowing into the Indian Ocean from Africa. The river is 3,540 km long and flows through Zambia, Angola, Namibia, Botswana, and Mozambique. The most noted feature of this river is Victoria Falls. What is this river called?

3) It is Europe's second-longest river, runs through the largest number of countries in the world (the Nile is second with 9 countries). Originating in Germany, it flows southeast for 2,850 km (1,770 mi), passing through or bordering Austria, Slovakia, Hungary, Croatia, Serbia, Romania, Bulgaria, Moldova, and Ukraine before draining into the Black Sea. What is this river?

4) It is the longest river in Asia. Its drainage basin comprises one-fifth of the land area of China and is home to nearly one-third of the country's population. What is this river?

5) It originates in the Tibetan Plateau in China and runs through China's Yunan Province, Burma, Laos, Thailand, Cambodia, and Vietnam. Some important cities in Southeast Asia are located along its path, including Vientiane (capital of Laos) and Phnom Penh (capital of Cambodia). This river plays a major role in sustaining the farming and inland fisheries. What is its name?

6) It is a 1,600 km long river that begins in Angola, where it is known by the Portuguese name Rio Cubango. Farther south, it forms part of the border between Angola and Namibia, and then flows into Botswana, draining into the Moremi Game Reserve. What is this river?

7) It is a river that is one of the longest rivers in the world. It flows northeast and then north from its source in the Baikal Mountains south of the Central Siberian Plateau, The navigation of this river is only possible from May to October as it is covered by a thick layer of ice rest of the year. What is it?

8) It is the longest river system in Canada and includes the second-largest drainage basin of any North American river after the Mississippi. There are Water mammals such as beavers and muskrats are extremely common in the Delta and surrounding areas of muskeg. And also is it a calving area for beluga whales. name this river?

9) It is found within the Mid-Atlantic region of the United States and flows from the Highlands into the Chesapeake Bay. It passes the capital of the United States. What is this river?

10) It is Australia's longest river with 2,508 km in length, being one of the major river systems on one of the driest continents on Earth, it has signed it has significant cultural relevance to Aboriginal Australians. What is this river?

Quiz 03: Mix Geography Quiz

Questions

1) What is the name of the desert located within Argentina and Chile?

2) What is the name of the strip of land between Israel and palatine, which was has given rise to an unending dispute between these two countries?

3) The world's largest wetland system by land area is found in Latin America. This wetland includes parts of Brazil, Paraguay, and Bolivia and is fed by the Rio Paraguay. What is the name of this wetland?

4) It is a Russian Oblast located on the Baltic coast. It forms the most western part of Russia, and has no land connection to the rest of the country, and is surrounded by Poland, Lithuania, and the Baltic Sea. What is this Oblast?

5) It is a region of the Atlantic Ocean bounded by four currents forming an ocean gyre. It is the only sea in the world without a coastline?

6) With an average elevation exceeding 4,500 meters (14,800 ft) and being surrounded by imposing mountain ranges that harbor the world's two highest summits, Mount Everest and K2, Which Plateau is often referred to as "the Roof of the World"?

7) Located in the South Zone of the city of Rio de Janeiro, Brazil. It is most prominently known for its 4 km (2.5 miles) Balneario beach, which is one of the most famous in the world. What is this beach?

8) It is a peninsula on the Gulf of Guinea that lies between the Cross River estuary, near the city of Calabar in the west of the Bight of Biafra, and the Rio del Ray estuary on the east. It is governed by Cameroon, following the transfer of sovereignty from neighboring Nigeria as a result of a judgment by the International Court of Justice. What is the name of this peninsula??

9) What is the deepest oceanic trench on Earth with 10,984m deep and the southern end of a small slot-shaped valley in its floor known as the Challenger Deep?

10) Located in the eastern Karakoram range in the Himalaya Mountains, this glacier is being claimed by both Pakistan and India. At 70 km (43 miles) long, it is the longest glacier in the Karakoram and second-longest in the world's non-polar areas. What is this glacier called?

Quiz 04: Islands

Questions

1) This Caribbean island makes up the principal territory for two independent nations Haiti & Dominican Republic. It is the second-largest island in the Caribbean after Cuba. Name this island?

2) This island is a part of Micronesia in the South Pacific, is the world's smallest independent island nation. It is a phosphate rock island, with deposits close to the surface, which was extracted for several decades in the 20th Century before the island ran out of phosphate. What is this island state's name?

3) Greenland covers an area of 2,166,086 square kilometers, which makes it the world's largest island that is not a continent. Which European country is Greenland an autonomous part of?

4) The eruption of Mount Pelee in 1902 is the worst volcanic disaster in 20 th century which killed more than 30000 people. In which Caribbean island is this volcano located?

5) With an area of 592,800 square kilometers what is the world's second-largest island country, after Indonesia?

6) They are an archipelago in the northeastern Indian Ocean about 130 km (81 mi) southwest off the coasts of Myanmar's Ayeyarwady Region. It is a part of India that was occupied by the Japanese in WW II. What is this island?

7) It is the southernmost territory of the United States and one of two U.S. territories south of the Equator, along with the uninhabited Jarvis Island. What is this US territory?

8) Guadal canal is one of the main islands of a country in the South Pacific Ocean. What is this island country?

9) Also known as "Land of Fire", it is an archipelago off the southernmost tip of the South American mainland, across the Strait of Magellan. What is this island which is divided between Chile and Argentina?

10) With an area of 8,336 km2 (3,219 sq mi) and a coastline of 1,046 km (650 mi), This is the largest and most populous of the Greek islands. It bounds the southern border of the Aegean Sea,) to the north and the Libyan Sea to the south. What is this island?

Quiz 05: Cities & States

Questions

1) What is the closest city to the equator?

2) What is the most populated state in India as well as the most populous country subdivision in the world?

3) Located high with an elevation of 3356ft in the east Pyrenees, between France and Spain, What is the highest capital city in Europe?

4) What is the smallest U.S. state by area?

5) This city s a city in southeastern Uzbekistan and among the oldest continuously inhabited cities in Central Asia. Prospering from its location on the Silk Road between China and the Mediterranean Sea, at times It was one of the largest cities of Central Asia. What is this city?

6) It is the city, port, and naval base on Navarino Island in Chile that faces the Beagle Channel. It is considered the southernmost city in the world. What is the name of this city?

7) It is the newest state of India that was created in 2014. The area was separated from the northwestern part of Andhra Pradesh as the newly formed state with Hyderabad as its capital. What is this Indian State?

8) Located in Peru, it is a town in the Peruvian Andes near a gold mine. At up to 5,100 m (16,700 ft; 3.2 mi) above sea level, it is the highest permanent settlement in the world. What is the name of this town?

9) There were nine members in the Federation of the Arab Emirates, located in the southeast of the Arabian Peninsula. When the British ended the protectorate arrangement in 1971, seven of them joined together to form the United Arab Emirates, UAE. Which two states chose to go their separate ways, and are today small but prosperous independent states?

10) It is the largest city in Turkey and the fifth-largest city in the world by population, is considered European, yet it occupies two different continents. One part lies in Europe and the other part lies in Asia. What is this city?

Quiz 06: Mountains

Questions

1) What is the highest and most extensive mountain range system that lies entirely in Europe?

2) With an elevation of 6214ft, What is the highest peak of the Urals in Russia?

3) With a height of 4413ft above sea level What is the highest mountain in the United Kingdom?

4) It is a flat-topped mountain forming a prominent landmark overlooking the city of Cape Town in South Africa. It is a significant tourist attraction, with many visitors using the cableway or hiking to the top. Name this mountain?

5) It is a mountain range between Spain and France. Reaching a height of 3,404 meters (11,168 ft.), it extends for about 491 km (305 mi) from its union with the Cantabrian Mountains to the Mediterranean Sea, for the most part, the main crest forms a divide between Spain and France, with the microstate of Andorra sandwiched in between. What is this mountain range?

6) It is the highest mountain in Europe. As the highest peak in the Caucasus Mountains, the dormant volcano rises 5,642 m (18,510 ft) above sea level, and is the highest stratovolcano in Eurasia. What is this mountain?

7) Rising 396 m (1,299 ft) above the harbor, it is a peak situated in Rio de Janeiro, Brazil, at the mouth of Guanabara Bay on a peninsula that juts out into the Atlantic Ocean. This became part of a World Heritage Site declared by UNESCO in 2012 and known worldwide for its cableway and panoramic views of the city and beyond. What is this peak?

8) It is located on the China–Pakistan border between Baltistan in the Gilgit-Baltistan region of northern Pakistan, at 8,611 meters (28,251 ft) above sea level, is the second-highest mountain in the world. What is it?

9) Located in Tanzania it is the tallest summit of the African continent, and the highest single free-standing mountain in the world: 5,895 meters (19,341 ft) above sea level and about 4,900 meters (16,100 ft) above its plateau base. What is it?

10)Located in Pakistan this is the ninth-highest mountain in the world at 8,126 meters (26,660 ft) above sea level. is known to be a difficult climb, and has earned the nickname Killer Mountain for its high number of climber fatalities. What is this mountain?

Quiz 07: Straits and Lakes

Questions

1) Which Strait separate of Italy and Sicily?

2) What body of water separates Australia and Papua New Guinea?

3) Located in southern Siberia, Russia What is the world's deepest lake with a maximum depth of 1,642 m which is home to thousands of species of plants and animals, and also home to Buryat tribes?

4) Also known as the Pink lake What is the lake situated in Senegal that is named for its pink waters caused by Dunaliella salina algae and is known for its high salt content, up to 40% in some areas.?

5) This strait separates the North and South Islands of New Zealand and connects the Tasman Sea on the northwest with the South Pacific Ocean on the southeast. What is it?

6) Situated in the Andes on the border of Bolivia and Peru, with a surface elevation of 12,507 ft. What is the "highest navigable lake" in the world?

7) It is of the world's narrowest straits used for international navigation. It is a narrow, natural strait and internationally significant waterway in northwestern Turkey that forms part of the continental boundary between Europe and Asia, and separates Asian Turkey from European Turkey. What is this strait?

8) In terms of volume, It is the world's ninth-largest continental lake that is divided among Kenya, Tanzania, and Uganda. What is the name of this lake?

9) What is the name of the strait between Yemen on the Arabian Peninsula, and Djibouti and Eritrea in the Horn of Africa that connects the Red Sea to the Gulf of Aden?

10) Scientists believe that an ancient lake hidden beneath West Antarctica's ice sheet may reveal vital clues about climate change and future sea level rises. The ice sheet covering the lake has trapped the Earth's geothermal heat, preventing it from freezing. What is the name of this underground lake?

Quiz 08: Mix Geography Quiz 02

Questions

1) It is India's smallest state by area and the fourth-smallest by population. Panaji is the state's capital, while Vasco da Gama is its largest city. What is this state?

2) What is the longest continental mountain range in the world, forming a continuous highland along the western edge of South America?

3) Easter Island, a Polynesian island in the southeastern Pacific Ocean, is also known as Rapa Nui or Isla de Pascua. It is considered to be the most isolated island in the world and home to one of the world's greatest cultural mysteries – the giant stone statues. Which Latin American country today administers this island, although it is located more than 3,600 kilometers (2,200 miles) off of its coast?

4) The Dolomites are a mountain range also known as the "Pale Mountains", take their name from the carbonate rock dolomite. In which European country are these mountains located?

5) It is a Caribbean country located on the northeastern coast of Central America. It is bordered to the north by Mexico, to the east by the Caribbean Sea, and the south and west by Guatemala. It is the only South American country that does not border the Pacific?

6) The Suez Canal is an artificial sea-level waterway in Egypt, connecting the Mediterranean Sea to the Red Sea through the Isthmus of Suez. Name its two ends?

7) Also known as the Great Indian Desert, is a large arid region in the northwestern part of the Indian subcontinent that covers an area of 200,000 km2 (77,000 sq mi) and forms a natural boundary between India and Pakistan. What is this dessert?

8) The Lucayan Archipelago is an island group comprising the Commonwealth of The Bahamas and another the British Overseas Territory. What is the name of this territory?

9) Surrounded by the South China Sea to the north and northwest this island is the third-largest island in the world and the largest island in Asia. It is divided into three countries. Malaysia and Brunei in the north, and Indonesia to the south. What is this Island?

10) It is a large sandstone rock formation in Australia and also one of Australia's most recognizable natural landmarks and has been a popular destination for tourists since the late 1930s. It is notable for appearing to change color at different times of the day and year. What is the name of it?

Quiz 09: Countries of the World 02

Questions

1) Timbuktu is a town in West Africa situated 15 km (9 miles) north of the River Niger on the southern edge of the Sahara Desert. In which modern-day African state is Timbuktu a provincial town?

2) The Ionian Islands are a group of islands that are traditionally called the Heptanese. what country administrate these islands?

3) The tallest summit of the African continent, Mount Kilimanjaro is located in which country?

4) This independent island nation in the central Pacific Ocean. comprises 32 atolls and one raised coral island, Banaba. It is the only country in the world to be situated in all four cardinal hemispheres. Name this country?

5) It is the second-smallest sovereign state in the world, after Vatican City. It is bordered by France to the north, east, and west, and the Mediterranean Sea to the south and is widely recognized for being one of the most expensive and wealthiest places in the world. What is this country?

6) Skorga, Vinnufossen, and Balaifossen are among the 10 highest waterfalls in the world. All of them are situated within a single country. What is this country?

7) The Darvaza gas crater, also known as the Door to Hell or Gates of Hell, is a natural gas field that collapsed into a cavern in Derweze.In which country it is located?

8) A certain western African country was created in the 1800s for all former slaves in the Americas who were freed and wanted to return to their original home continent. The country was formally declared in 1847, and established a government modeled on that of the United States., What is this country?

9) What is the smallest country in Central America and entirely located on the western side, making it the only Central American country without a coastline to the Caribbean Sea?

10) Bordered by Burma & China to the northwest, Vietnam to the east, Cambodia to the south, and Thailand to the west, this country is the only landlocked country in Southeast Asia. What is this country?

Quiz:10 Mix Geography Quiz 02

Questions

1) It is an active stratovolcano on the east coast of Sicily, Italy, in the Metropolitan City of Catania, between the cities of Messina and Catania. It lies above the convergent plate margin between the African Plate and the Eurasian Plate. It is one of the tallest active volcanoes in Europe. What is this volcano?

2) It is a series of seven cataracts, each no more than 5 m (16 ft) high, extending over more than 100 km in the Orientale Province of the Democratic Republic of the Congo. The seven cataracts have a total drop of 61 m (200 ft). They form the largest waterfall by volume of annual flow rate in the world. What is the name of this waterfall?

3) The Japanese archipelago comprises four islands. The largest of the four main islands is lying between the Pacific Ocean and the Sea of Japan. It is also the most populous main island of Japan. What is it?

4) It is a city and chief port of Kenya, situated on a coralline island in a bay of the Indian Ocean. This city is the center of coastal tourism in Kenya. And also an important economic center. What is this famous city?

27

5) What is the name was given to the international land border between the countries of Afghanistan and Pakistan that western end runs to the border with Iran and the eastern end to the border with China?

6) What is the mountain range at the intersection of Europe and Asia? Stretching between the Black Sea and the Caspian Sea?

7) Niagara Falls is a group of three waterfalls spanning the border between the province of Ontario in Canada and the state of New York in the United States. Two of these waterfalls are American Falls and Bridal Veil Falls. What is the name of the other waterfall which is also the largest of them?

8) What is the only country that passes through both the equator and the tropic of Capricorn?

9) It is a deep submarine depression in the eastern Indian Ocean that extends some 2,000 miles in a northwest-southeast arc along the southwestern and southern Indonesian archipelago with a maximum depth of 7,290 meters. ts maximum depth is the deepest point in the Indian Ocean. By what name is this trench called?

10) Situated on the Neva River, at the head of the Gulf of Finland on the Baltic Sea, it is the most populous city on the Baltic Sea, as well as the world's northernmost city with over 1 million residents. What is this city?

Quiz 11:History Quiz 01

Questions

1) Who was the first Roman emperor, reigning from 27 BC until he died in AD 14?

2) Which great clash of arms, fought in central-western France on 10 October 732 AD, helped lay the foundations of the Carolingian Empire and Frankish domination of western Europe for the next century?

3) Located in Northern Afghanistan, Balkh is described by Arabs as the 'Mother of Cities'. Continually inhabited since 1500 BC, it had reached its peak during an earlier period of settlement (between 2500-1900BC). A name well known in a zoological context, how was the city known in the time of Darius and Alexander the Great?

4) He was Roman emperor from 306 to 337. He built a new imperial residence at Byzantium and renamed the city Constantinople (now Istanbul) after himself. Name this emperor?

5) It was a Korean dynastic kingdom that lasted for approximately five centuries and It was the last dynastic kingdom of Korea. It was founded by Yi Seong-gye in July 1392 and replaced by the Korean Empire in October 1897. What is the name of this dynastic kingdom?

6) It is the first written language that was born around 3,300 BC and used cuneiform (wedge-shaped) elements instead of the previous pictograms, and the writing direction was changed to follow left-to-right in horizontal rows. What is this language?

7) During his reign, the Aztec Empire reached its greatest size. he was killed during the initial stages of the Spanish conquest of the Aztec Empire when conquistador Hernán Cortés and his men fought to take over the Aztec capital Tenochtitlán. Name this emperor?

8) He was the founder and first Great Khan and Emperor of the Mongol Empire, which became the largest contiguous empire in history after his death. He came to power by uniting many of the nomadic tribes of Northeast Asia. Who is he?

9) This 82day long battle in the Pacific War of World War II resulted in the highest number of casualties in the Pacific Theatre during World War II. Japan lost over 100,000 soldiers and the Allies suffered more than 65,000 casualties of all kinds. Code named Operation Iceberg, by what name do we now identify this battle?

10) He was an Anglo-Irish soldier and Tory statesman who was one of the leading military and political figures of 19th-century Britain, serving twice as prime minister. He ended the Napoleonic Wars when he defeated Napoleon at the Battle of Waterloo in 1815. Who was he?

Quiz 12: Asian Politics 01

Questions

1) He was an Indian independence activist, lawyer, scholar, and subsequently, the first President of India, in office from 1950 to 1962. Who is he?

2) Which famous scientist was offered the presidency of Israel but turned down the offer?

3) Considered to be the driving force behind the independence of Bangladesh, Who was swept to power and became president of Bangladesh?

4) He was a Chinese politician, physician, and political philosopher, who served as the provisional first president of the Republic of China & referred to as the "Father of the Nation" in the Republic of China for his instrumental role in the overthrow of the Qing dynasty during the Xinhai Revolution. Who is he?

5) He is a Bhutanese politician who became Bhutan's first-ever elected Prime Minister in 2008 after his political party Druk Phuensum Tshogpa won 45 of the 47 seats in the National Assembly of Bhutan. Name him?

6) He was a Filipino statesman who served as the seventh President of the Philippines, from December 30, 1953, until he died in an aircraft disaster. Name him?

7) He's one of the leading founding fathers of Pakistan. In 1947, he became the first Prime Minister of Pakistan, He also held cabinet portfolio as the first foreign, defense, and frontier regions minister from 1947 until his assassination in 1951. Who was he?

8) He was a prominent leader of Indonesia's nationalist movement during the Dutch colonial period and spent over a decade under Dutch detention until released by the invading Japanese forces in World War II. In 1945 he become the first president of Indonesia and rule the country till 1967. Who is he?

9) In 1973, Nobel Peace Prize was jointly awarded to the then US Secretary of State Henry Kissinger and a (then North) Vietnamese diplomat and politician for 'negotiating the Vietnam peace accord". The Vietnamese winner said that he was not in a position to accept the Nobel Peace Prize, citing the situation in Vietnam as his reason. Who was he?

10) She was a Sri Lankan stateswoman who became the world's first female prime minister in 1960. In 1972 she oversaw the drafting of a new constitution and the formation of the Sri Lankan republic. She served three terms: 1960–1965, 1970–1977, and 1994–2000 as the prime minister. Name her?

Quiz 13: European Politics 01

Questions

1) Who was the first prime minister of Great Britain?

2) Who is the Italian prime minister who was kidnapped by the far-left terrorist group Red Brigades and killed after 55 days of captivity?

3) Who was the Portuguese statesman and economist who served as Prime Minister of Portugal from 1932 to 1968?

4) Who is both the oldest person to serve as Prime Minister of England and the only Prime Minister to have served four terms?

5) The eighth and last leader of the Soviet Union, Widely considered one of the most significant figures of the second half of the 20th century, He was the recipient of a wide range of awards—including the Nobel Peace Prize and was widely praised for his pivotal role in ending the Cold War. Who is he?

6) She led the Orange Revolution and was the first woman appointed Prime Minister of Ukraine. She supports Ukraine's integration into the European Union and strongly opposes the membership of Ukraine in the Russia-led Eurasian Customs Union. She supports NATO membership in Ukraine. Name her?

7) She has been described as the "Iron Lady" of Israeli politics & the world's fourth and Israel's first and only woman to hold the office of Prime Minister. Who is she?

8) He was a Cypriot clergyman and politician who served as the archbishop and primate of the autocephalous Church of Cyprus (1950–1977) and as the first president of Cyprus (1960–1977). In his three terms as president, he survived four assassination attempts and a coup d'état. Who is he?

9) He was a French army officer and statesman who led Free France against Nazi Germany in World War II and chaired the Provisional Government of the French Republic from 1944 to 1946 to reestablish democracy in France. He was elected President of France in 1958 and held until his resignation in 1969. Name him?

10) He was a German Nazi politician and Reich Minister of Propaganda of Nazi Germany from 1933 to 1945. He was one of Adolf Hitler's closest and most devoted associates and was known for his skills in public speaking and his deeply virulent anti-Semitism. He advocated progressively harsher discrimination, including the extermination of the Jews in the Holocaust. Who is he?

Quiz 14: African Politics 01

Questions

1) Who was a politician who served as the first President of Zambia from 1964 to 1991?

2) Who was the politician who served as the first President of Algeria from 1963 to 1965?

3) She was the prime minister of the Central African Republic from 1975 to 1976. She was the first woman to serve as prime minister of an African nation. Who is she?

4) He was an Egyptian politician who served as the second President of Egypt, from 1954 until he died in 1970. His popularity in Egypt and the Arab world skyrocketed after he nationalized the Suez Canal and his political victory in the subsequent Suez Crisis. Who is he?

5) He is a Congolese politician and independence leader who served as the first Prime Minister of the independent Democratic Republic of the Congo from June until September 1960. He led the Congolese National Movement (MNC) party from 1958 until his assassination. Name him?

6) He is the president of Cameroon since 1982. He introduced political reforms within the context of a one-party system in the 1980s. Under serious pressure, he accepted the introduction of multiparty politics in the early 1990s. He won the contentious 1992 presidential election with 40% of the plural, single-ballot vote and was re-elected by large margins in 1997, 2004, 2011, and 2018. Who is he?

7) He was Kenya's first indigenous head of government and played a significant role in the transformation of Kenya from a colony of the British Empire into an independent republic. Name this politician who was the first president of Kenya from 1964 to 1978?

8) The Nobel Peace Prize 1993 was awarded jointly to Nelson Mandela and then the serving President of South Africa "for their work for the peaceful termination of the apartheid regime, and for laying the foundations for a new democratic South Africa". Who was he?

9) Who was the Nigerian military general who served as the military head of the state of Nigeria from 1993 until he died in 1998? In 1993, He became the first Nigerian Army officer to attain the rank of a full military general without skipping a single rank?

10) He was Zimbabwe's first head of state after the Lancaster House Agreement that led to the country's independence. In 1987, he stepped down as President and was succeeded by Prime Minister Robert Mugabe, who became the country's executive president. Who is he?

Quiz 15: U.S presidents

Questions

1) He served as the 26th president of the United States from 1901 to 1909. He took office as vice president in March 1901 and assumed the presidency at age 42 after McKinley was assassinated. He remains the youngest person to become President of the United States. Who is he?

2) He was the 27th president of the United States (1909–1913) and the tenth Chief Justice of the United States (1921–1930), the only person to have held both offices. Name Him?

3) He was the 37th president of the United States, serving from 1969 until 1974. He imposed wage and price controls for 90 days and established the Environmental Protection Agency. Because of the Watergate scandal, he has resigned from office and became the only U.S president to do so. Name him?

4) This U.S President won a record four presidential elections and became a central figure in world events during the first half of the 20th century. He directed the federal government during most of the Great Depression, implementing his New Deal domestic agenda in response to the worst economic crisis in U.S. history. Name him?

5) He was the 40th president of the United States from 1981 to 1989 and became a highly influential voice of modern conservatism. Before his presidency, he was a Hollywood actor and union leader. He holds the record for winning the most electoral votes of any U.S. president, 525, or 97.6% of the 538 votes in the Electoral College. Name him?

6) During World War II, he became a five-star general in the Army and served as Supreme Commander of the Allied Expeditionary Force in Europe. He was responsible for planning and supervising the invasion of North Africa in Operation Torch in 1942–43 and the successful invasion of Normandy in 1944–45 from the Western Front. Name this person who served as the US President from 1953 to 1961?

7) He led the nation through the American Civil War, the country's greatest moral, constitutional, and political crisis. He succeeded in preserving the Union, abolishing slavery, bolstering the federal government, and modernizing the U.S. economy. In 1865 he was assassinated while attending a play at Ford's Theatre. Who is he?

8) He held the US presidency for only 895 days which is the shortest in U.S. history for any president who did not die in office. And also he is the only person to have served as both vice president and president without being elected to either office by the Electoral College. Who is this US President?

9) He is an American military officer and politician who served as the ninth president of the United States in 1841. He died of typhoid, pneumonia, or paratyphoid fever 31 days into his term, becoming the first president to die in office and the shortest-serving president in U.S. history. Name him?

10) He is the wealthiest president in U.S. history, even after adjusting for inflation. He is also the first president who did not serve in the military or hold any government office before becoming president. Who is he?

Quiz 16: History Quiz 02

Questions

1) Only months into his reign, This English king caused a constitutional crisis by proposing to Wallis Simpson, an American who had divorced her first husband and was seeking a divorce from her second. When it became apparent he could not marry Wallis and remain on the throne, he abdicated and was succeeded by his younger brother, George VI. Who is this king?

2) Fall of Constantinople' in 1453 marked the end of the Roman Empire, and at that time it was the capital of the Byzantine Empire. When the city was captured by Ottoman Turks, before and after the siege several Greek and Non-Greek intellectuals fled the city particularly to Italy. It is said that the Renaissance in Europe was fueled by the 'Fall of Constantinople'. What is the present name of the city "Constantinople"?

3) He was a king of Macedon, a state in northern ancient Greece. Tutored by Aristotle until the age of 16. By the age of thirty, he had created one of the largest empires of the ancient world, stretching from the Ionian Sea to the Himalayas. He was undefeated in battle and is considered one of history's most successful commanders. This warrior king died in Babylon in 323 BC, without executing a series of planned campaigns that would have begun with an invasion of Arabia. Who is this emperor?

4) He was the first ruler to be crowned as Tsar of all Russia transforming Russia into a multiethnic and multiconfessional state spanning almost one billion acres, he managed countless changes in the progression from a medieval state to an empire and emerging regional power. Who is the 1st Tsar of Russia?

5) Considered as one of the bloodiest battles in human history, this World War I battle in 1916 saw the introduction of battle tanks for modern warfare. The British and French offensive to penetrate German-controlled territory in France ended with inconclusive results despite over 1million casualties. Name this famous battle fought infamous river Bank in France?

6) Regarded as one of the greatest naval mariners in history, He was an English flag officer in the Royal Navy. His inspirational leadership brought about several decisive British naval victories, particularly during the Napoleonic Wars. He was fatally shot in 1805, shortly before his victory at the Battle of Trafalgar. name him?

7) On 6th August 1945, during the final stages of World War II, the USA dropped its first of 2 atomic bombs on the Japanese city of Hiroshima. The airplane which dropped the bomb was a Boeing B-29 Superfortress bomber, which was named after the mother of its pilot Paul Tibbets. What was the name given to this Airplane?

8) The Swiss businessman Jean Henri Dunant was visiting a small town in Northern Italy in 1859 when French and Sardinian troops faced the advancing Austrian troops in a nearby location. Witnessing the level of atrocities and lack of attention given to the wounded at the subsequent battle led him to form International Red Cross in 1862. Name this famous battle?

9) He was the Sixth and best-known ruler of the 1st dynasty of Babylon. He is better known for having issued a code of justice, which he claimed to have received from Shamash, the Babylonian god of justice. Who was he?

10) It was located at the junction of Friedrichstrasse and Zimmerstrasse and was the best-known Berlin Wall crossing point between East Berlin and West Berlin during the Cold War. After the Cold War ended Germany reunified, the building at this famous junction became a tourist attraction and is now located in the Allied Museum. What was this junction called by the Western allies during the Cold War?

Quiz 17: Asian Politics 02

Questions

1) Who was the first prime minister of Malaysia?

2) He was the first Premier of the People's Republic of China. serving from October 1949 until his death in January 1976. He served under Chairman Mao Zedong and was instrumental in the Communist Party's rise to power, and later in consolidating its control, forming foreign policy, and developing the Chinese economy. Who is he?

3) He is one of the most controversial leaders of the 20th century, he ruled the Philippines as a dictator under martial law from 1972 until 1981and kept most of his martial law powers until he was deposed in 1986. Who is he?

4) This Communist revolutionist turned mass murderer killed and was indirectly responsible for the deaths of approximately 2.5 million of his country's people. He was one of the Khmer rouges who never faced any trial until he died in 1998. Name him?

5) He became the Executive Head of the World Zionist Organization in 1946 and was the first to sign the Israeli Declaration of Independence. Later he was referred to as "Israel's founding father". Name this first Prime Minister of Israel?

6) He served as Prime Minister of Japan from 1964 to 1972. He brought Japan into the Nuclear Non-Proliferation Treaty, for which he received the Nobel Peace Prize in 1974. Who is he?

7) He is recognized as Singapore's founding father, credited with rapidly transitioning the country from a "developing third world country into a developed first world country within a single generation" under his leadership. Name him?

8) He was the 1st prime minister of India and was a principal leader of the Indian independence movement in the 1930s and 1940s. He promoted parliamentary democracy, secularism, and science and technology during the 1950s, powerfully influencing India's arc as a modern nation. Name this great politician who was also a widely admired author, where his books written in prison, such as Letters from a Father to His Daughter (1929 and The Discovery of India (1946), were read around the world.

9) This Burmese revolutionary, nationalist, and founder of the modern Burmese army is recognized as the leading architect of Burmese independence and the founder of the Union of Burma. Affectionately known as 'Bogyoke' (General), he is still widely admired by the Burmese people. He was assassinated in July 1947, But his place in history is assured both from his legacy and due to the political struggle of his daughter, Aung San Suu Kyi, who was only two when her father died aged 32. Who was he?

10) He seized power as head of the army during a bloodless coup against President Abdus Sattar in 1982 and President in 1983. Name this former president of Bangladesh?

Quiz 18: European Politics 02

Questions

1) He was a Romanian communist politician and dictator who served as the countries head of state from 1967 to 1989. He was overthrown and executed in Romanian Revolution in December 1989 along with her wife Elena. Name him?

2) He was one of the oldest elected leaders in world history. As the first post-war Chancellor of Germany (West Germany) from 1949 to 1963, he led his country from the ruins of World War II to a powerful and prosperous nation. Name him?

3) He was the chief architect of the Socialist Federal Republic of Yugoslavia (SFRY), serving as both Prime Minister (1944–1963), President (later President for Life) (1953–1980), and Marshal of Yugoslavia). Despite being one of the founders of Cominform, he became the first Cominform member to defy Soviet hegemony in 1948. Who was he?

4) He was a British Tory statesman who served as Prime Minister of the United Kingdom from October 1809 until his assassination in May 1812. He is the only British prime minister to have been assassinated. So far he is the only Solicitor General or Attorney General to have become Prime Minister. Who is he?

5) He was a Polish pianist and composer who became a spokesman for Polish independence. In 1919, he was the Poland Prime Minister and foreign minister during which he signed the Treaty of Versailles, which ended World War I. Who is he?

6) Upon his return to Earth, Yuri Gagarin, then 27, became an instant celebrity. He was escorted in a long motorcade of high-ranking officials through the streets of Moscow to the Kremlin where he was awarded the highest Soviet honor, the title of Hero of the Soviet Union, by the then Soviet premier who was a strong supporter of the Soviet Space Programme. Who was he?

7) He served as the President of the Federal Republic of Yugoslavia from 1997 to 2000. He became the first sitting head of state to be charged with war crimes. During the 1990s, numerous anti-government and antiwar protests took place. Who is he?

8) He was a British statesman and Liberal politician. In a career lasting over 60 years, he served for 12 years as Prime Minister of the United Kingdom, spread over four terms beginning in 1868 and ending in 1894. Who is he?

9) He was a French politician who served as President of France from 1969 until he died in 1974. He had long been a top aide to President Charles de Gaulle; as head of state, he was a moderate conservative who repaired France's relationship with the United States and maintained positive relations with the newly independent former colonies in Africa. Who is he?

10) The Berlin Wall was erected by former East Germany beginning on August 13, 1961, to completely cut off West Berlin from surrounding East Germany and from East Berlin. The Wall symbolized the Iron Curtain between communist East Germany and capitalist West Germany during the Cold War. It was finally broken down on November 9, 1989, as a result of weeks of people's agitations. Name the East German leader who ordered the Berlin Wall's construction in 1961?

Quiz 19: World Politics

Questions

1) He was an Egyptian politician who served as the third President of Egypt, he engaged in negotiations with Israel, culminating in the Egypt–Israel Peace Treaty; this won him and Menachem Begin the Nobel Peace Prize, making Sadat the first Muslim Nobel laureate. In 1981 he was assassinated. Who is him?

2) Who is the Congolese revolutionary and politician who served as the third President of the Democratic Republic of the Congo from May 17, 1997, when he overthrew Mobutu Sese Seko, until his assassination on January 16, 2001?

3) She is a long-time women's rights activist, she became the first female head state in southern Africa and the third in the whole African continent when she became President of Malawi in April 2012. Who is this progressive African leader?

4) Who is the Central African political and military leader who served as the second president of the Central African Republic and as the emperor of its successor state, the Central African Empire, from his Saint-Sylvestre coup d'état on 1 January 1966 until overthrown in a subsequent coup in 1979?

5) She is a Liberian politician who served as the 24th President of Liberia from 2006 to 2018. She was the first elected female head of state in Africa and won the Nobel Peace Prize in 2011, in recognition of her efforts to bring women into the peacekeeping process?

6) He was an Argentine Marxist revolutionary, physician, author, guerrilla leader, diplomat, and military theorist. A major figure of the Cuban Revolution, his stylized visage has become a ubiquitous countercultural symbol of rebellion and global insignia in popular culture. In 1967 he was captured by CIA-assisted Bolivian forces and summarily executed. Name him?

7) On July 16, 1790, the Residence Act approved the creation of a capital Washington, D.C located along the Potomac River on the USA's East Coast. While the capital was being constructed, a different city served as the temporary capital of the USA. What was this city?

8) He was an American political scientist, diplomat, and leading actor in the mid-20th Century decolonization process and US civil rights movement. He received the 1950 Nobel Peace Prize for his late 1940s mediation in Israel and became the first person of African descent to be awarded a Nobel Prize. Who was he?

9) He led the Australian Labor Party (ALP) to power for the first time in 23 years at the 1972 election. He won the 1974 election before being controversially dismissed by the Governor-General of Australia, Sir John Kerr, at the climax of the 1975 Australian constitutional crisis. He remains the only Australian prime minister to have been removed from office in this manner. Name him?

10) What was the code name given for the invasion of the Soviet Union by Nazi Germany and some of its Axis allies, which started on Sunday, 22 June 1941, during World War II?

Quiz 20: American Politics

Questions

1) Who was the military dictator overthrown by Fidel Castro in the Cuban revolution?

2) Name the US vice president who resigned from his position in 1973 due to Tax fraud scandal?

3) He is the only sitting member of the United States House of Representatives to be elected to the presidency. He was elected as the 20th president of the United States, serving from March 4, 1881, until his death by assassination six and a half months later. Who is he?

4) She is an Argentine politician who served as President of Argentina from 1974 to 1976. She holds the distinction of having been the first woman to have had the title of "President", as opposed to a queen or prime minister. She served as president of Argentina from 1 July 1974 to 24 March 1976, at which time the military took over the government and placed her under house arrest for five years, before exiling her to Spain in 1981. Who is she?

5) He was a Chilean general, politician, and dictator who ruled Chile from 1973 to 1990. He seized power in Chile in a U.S.-backed coup d'état that toppled Allende's democratically elected Unidad Popular government and ended civilian rule. Name him?

6) He played a crucial role in forming the Insurrectionist faction, which united the FSLN and sparked the mass uprisings of 1978–1979, culminating in the Nicaraguan Revolution. He was the leader of Nicaragua from 1979 to 1990 and won the presidency again in 2007. Who is he?

7) She is a Canadian politician, who served as the 19th prime minister of Canada from June 25 to November 4, 1993. She is the first and only woman to hold the position. Name her?

8) This Argentine leader was appointed general by the first autonomous government of Argentina in 1810. He took part in the Argentine Wars of Independence and created the Flag of Argentina. Name him?

9) Who is the President of Costa Rica 1986-90 and again from 2006-10, who received the Nobel Peace Prize in 1987 for his efforts to end civil wars then raging in several other Central American countries?

10) She is a Colombian politician who was kidnapped by left-wing FARC guerrillas in 2002 while campaigning for the Presidency. She was rescued by Colombian security forces six and a half years later on 2 July 2008. The rescue operation, dubbed Operation Jaque. Who is she?

Quiz 21: Famous People 01

Questions

1) Who is the founder of the Scout Movement?

2) Who discover the tomb of King Tutankhamen in 1922?

3) Name the French sculptor who designed The Statue Of Liberty?

4) Who was the first African Nobel Peace Prize Laureate, who received the Prize in 1960?

5) Who was the first to complete a non-stop balloon flight around the globe, in a balloon named Breitling Orbiter 3?

6) The first Director-General of IMF was a national of Belgium, who served as Managing Director from May 1946 to May 1951. Who was he?

7) He was an American clergyman, activist, and prominent leader in the African American civil rights movement who won the Nobel Prize in 1964 at the age of 35. Who was this well-known advocate of racial equality and non-violence?

8) In 1961, the chartered UN plane carrying the then UN Secretary-General crashed in the African bush during a peace mission to Congo, killing all 15 persons aboard. The accident remained one of the Cold War's great mysteries. Name the Swedish diplomat, economist, and author who thus perished, the only UN chief to die on the job?

9) He is most known for the discoveries of the wrecks of the RMS Titanic in 1985, the battleship Bismarck in 1989, and the aircraft carrier USS Yorktown in 1998. Who is this professor of oceanography?

10) He was an American merchant, statesman, and prominent Patriot of the American Revolution. He served as president of the Second Continental Congress and was the first and third Governor of the Commonwealth of Massachusetts. He is remembered for his large and stylish signature on the United States Declaration of Independence. Name him?

Quiz 22: Successful Entrepreneurs

Questions

1) Who were the American biochemist and Confederate States Army veteran who is best known as the inventor of Coca-Cola?

2) He is an Indian billionaire business magnate, and the chairman, managing director, and largest shareholder of Reliance Industries Ltd. A Fortune Global 500 company and India's most valuable company by market value. He is the richest person in Asia with a net worth of US$81.1 billion, and as of October 2020. Name him?

3) This American businessman formed Standard Oil Company in 1870 and amassed a fortune from petroleum. When he retired in 1897, he had become the first American to amass a billion dollars and the richest man in the world. He spent the last 40 years of his life developing a systematic approach of targeted philanthropy, with foundations that had a major effect on medicine, education, and scientific research. In this process, he gave away most of his money to charities, keeping only 20 million dollars for himself before his death in 1937. Who was he?

4) Founded in 1975, Zara is one of the largest fashion retailing chains in the world and is owned by Inditex Group. Name the Spanish Billionaire who is the founder of Zara, and who is currently among the top ten billionaires in the world?

5) Name the key founder who in 2006 founded the leading social networking site "Twitter" which handled an average of 1.6 billion search queries per day?

6) He was an American industrialist and business magnate, By creating the first automobile that middle-class Americans could afford, he converted the automobile from an expensive curiosity into an accessible conveyance that profoundly impacted the landscape of the 20th century. Name him?

7) He is a famous fashion designer, best known for the Ralph Lauren Corporation, The maker of the world-famous clothing brand "Polo". He has become well known for his collection of rare automobiles, some of which have been displayed in museum exhibits. Who is he?

8) He is Nepal's first billionaire to be featured on the Forbes billionaires list but built most of his fortune overseas. He has a controlling stake in Nepal's Nabil Bank and a string of luxury hotels with India's Taj hotel chain. Name him?

9) He is a Mexican business magnate, who is the chairman of Telmex is a Mexican telecommunications company headquartered in Mexico City that provides telecommunications products and services in Mexico. He accounts for 40% of the listings on the Mexican Stock Exchange, while his net worth is equivalent to about 6 percent of Mexico's gross domestic product. Who is he?

10) He is a Hong Kong business magnate who is the world's leading port investor, developer, and operator of the largest health and beauty retailer in Asia and Europe. His conglomerate company Cheung Kong Holdings is influential in many sectors of the Hong Kong economy and made up 4% of the aggregate market capitalization of the Hong Kong Stock Exchange. Name him?

Quiz 23: Great Women

Questions

1) In the United States (US), the second Sunday of May is observed as Mothers' Day. This started with one woman, grief-stricken by her mother's death, sending letters to many prominent people, institutions, and companies in her country. President Woodrow Wilson read one of her letters and declared Mothers' Day. Who was this woman?

2) She was an Austrian and was a novelist and pacifist. She is depicted in the Austrian 2 Euro coin and formerly in the 1,000 schilling banknote. Name this lady who in 1905 became the first woman to receive the Nobel Peace Prize?

3) She was a French heiress, socialite, and businesswoman. She was one of the principal shareholders of L'Oréal. At the time of her death in 2017, she was the richest woman, and the 14th richest person in the world, with a net worth of US$44.3 billion. Name her?

4) She was a Dutch exotic dancer and courtesan who was convicted of being a spy for Germany during World War I. Despite her having admitted under interrogation to taking money to work as a German spy, many people still believe she was innocent. She was executed by firing squad in France. Name her?

5) She is a self-made billionaire who was once ranked by Forbes magazine as the richest African-American in the 20th Century. She is a spokesperson for many causes, owns her magazine O, cable television networks called OWN, a production company – and has been on television for over 25 years in the United States who is she?

6) This woman, an American teacher, was instrumental in using new techniques to teach the blind including the famous Helen Keller. This teacher's life was the basis for a television drama, Broadway play, and a Hollywood movie, all by the name The Miracle Worker. Who was this remarkable teacher?

7) Trained as a mathematician, this young aristocratic English woman wrote the first algorithm intended to be processed by a machine in 1843. She based them on Jacquard's punch-card idea and meant to be used on Charles Babbage's early mechanical general-purpose computer, the analytical engine. A visionary, she also foresaw a day when computers will go well beyond mere calculating or number-crunching. Who was she?

8) She was an English author, essayist, publisher, and writer of short stories who is regarded as one of the foremost modernist literary figures of that century. She was a member of the English Bloomsbury Group, and suffered repeated bouts of depression, and is believed to have been bipolar. Who is the author?

9) This Bangladeshi doctor turned writer has authored many works of fiction and poetry, but she became known worldwide when her 1993 novel 'Lajja' (Shame) was banned in her home country. She has been controversial owing to her feminist views and her criticism of Islam in particular and of religion in general. Under threat from religious fanatics, she has been living in exile in various countries. Who is she?

10) Who are the US politician and diplomats who served as the first female United States Secretary of State in U.S. history from 1997 to 2001 under President Bill Clinton?

Quiz 24: Famous People 02

Questions

1) Who became world-famous for making the first airplane flight across the English Channel, winning the prize of £1,000 offered by the Daily Mail newspaper?

2) Who was the first woman to swim the English Channel in both directions, setting a time record each time? She was also the first woman to swim the Catalina Channel, the Straits of Gibraltar, the Bosporus (one way), and the Dardanelles (round trip)?

3) Name the French poet and essayist who was the first winner of the Nobel Prize in Literature in 1901?

4) This English doctor was one of the most prolific serial killers in recorded history by proven murders with 250+ murders being positively ascribed to him. About 80% of his victims were women. His youngest victim was a 41-year-old man. Much of Britain's legal structure concerning health care and medicine was reviewed and modified as a direct and indirect result of his crimes and he is to date the only British doctor who has been found guilty of murdering his patients. Name him?

5) Reigning for 70 years and 126 days, He is both the second-longest reigning monarch of all time and the longest-reigning monarch to have reigned only as an adult. During his reign, he was served by a total of 30 prime ministers beginning with Pridi Banomyong and ending with Prayut Chan-o-cha. Name this monarch of Thailand?

6) The Battle of Saipan was a battle of the Pacific campaign of World War II, fought on the island of Saipan in the Mariana Islands from 15 June to 9 July 1944. That attack provoked the Unites States to get directly involved in the Second World War. Who was this Japanese admiral, who later committed suicide during the Battle of Saipan in July 1944?

7) This American agronomist, trained in plant pathology and genetics, introduced high-yielding wheat varieties and modern agricultural production techniques to Mexico, Pakistan, and India. He has been called "the Father of the Green Revolution", and is often credited with saving over a billion people worldwide from starvation. He was awarded the Nobel Peace Prize (1970Who is he?

8) This young aristocratic English woman wrote the first algorithm intended to be processed by a machine in 1843. She based them on Jacquard's punch-card idea and meant to be used on Charles Babbage's early mechanical general-purpose computer, the analytical engine. She is often regarded as the first to recognize the full potential of computers and as one of the first computer programmers. Who was she?

9) The Green Belt Movement is the name of the women-led conservation organization founded in 1977 in Kenya, which has spread across Africa and has planted 20 to 30 million trees on that continent. Who were a Kenyan social, environmental, and political activist and the first African woman to win the Nobel Prize? Who founded this organization?

10) The first President of the World Bank was an American financier, public official, and one-time Chairman of the US Federal Reserve from 1930 to 1933. He was also the publisher of the Washington Post newspaper. Although he served as World Bank president only for six months in 1946, he laid the foundation for the new institution drawing on his own practical experiences in government and investment banking. Who was he?

Quiz 25: Nobel Laureates

Questions

1) Who is the youngest Nobel Laureate who got the Peace Prize in 2014 at the age of just 17 years?

2) Name the French Novelist who was awarded the 1964 Nobel Prize in Literature despite attempting to refuse it, saying that he always declined official honors and that "a writer should not allow himself to be turned into an institution?

3) Who is the oldest recipient of the Nobel prize in Chemistry 2019 at the age of 97 years?

4) He is the author of Doctor Zhivago (1957), a novel that takes place between the Russian Revolution of 1905 and the Second World War. He was awarded the Nobel Prize for Literature in 1958, an event that enraged the Communist Party of the Soviet Union, which forced him to decline the prize. Who is he?

5) With the 1903 Nobel Prize in Physics and the 1911 Nobel Prize in Chemistry. Who is the only woman who has been honored twice?

6) He was the visionary, promoter, and co-founder of the Red Cross. In 1901 he received the first Nobel Peace Prize together with Frederic Passy, making Dunant the first Swiss Nobel laureate. Who is he?

7) Who was the British biochemist who twice won the Nobel Prize in Chemistry, one of only two people to have done so in the same category (the other is John Bardeen in physics?

8) Who is the only person to have been awarded two unshared Nobel Prizes – the 1954 Nobel Prize in Chemistry and the 1962 Nobel Peace Prize?

9) Who was the first Asian to win the Nobel Prize for literature?

10) Name the Canadian prime minister who won the Nobel Peace Prize in 1957 for organizing the United Nations Emergency Force to resolve the Suez Canal Crisis?

Quiz 26: Maritime Disasters

Questions

1) The world was shocked when the Titanic hit an iceberg at 11:40 p.m. on April 14, 1912, and sunk just a few hours later at 2:20 am on April 15. The "unsinkable" ship RMS Titanic sank on its maiden voyage, losing at least 1,517 lives, making it one of the deadliest maritime disasters in history. Although several ships received the Titanic's distress calls and changed their course to help, what is the name of the ship that first arrive for rescue?

2) It was a Japanese-built and Philippine-registered passenger ferry that sank after colliding with the oil tanker Vector on December 20, 1987. Official blame was directed at Vector, which was found to be unseaworthy and operating without a license, lookout, or qualified master. With an estimated death toll of 4,386 people and only 25 survivors, it remains the deadliest peacetime maritime disaster in history. What is the name of this ship?

3) It was a ferry vessel that was sunk as it was crossing from Tallinn to Stockholm in September 1994, killing 852 people. It is the second-deadliest peacetime sinking of a European ship, after the RMS Titanic, and the deadliest peacetime shipwreck to have occurred in European waters. What is this ship?

4) The sinking of this Cunard ocean liner occurred on, 7 May 1915 during the First World War, as Germany waged submarine warfare against the United Kingdom which had implemented a naval blockade of Germany. The ship was identified and torpedoed by the German U-boat U-20, took on a heavy starboard list, and sank in 18 minutes killing 1,198 and leaving 761 survivors. The sinking turned public opinion in many countries against Germany, contributed to the American entry into World War I, and became an iconic symbol in military recruiting campaigns of why the war was being fought. What is this ship?

5) It was a roll-on/roll-off (RORO) ferry that capsized moments after leaving the Belgian port of Zeebrugge on the night of 6 March 1987, killing 193 passengers and crew. Since the disaster, improvements have been made to the design of RORO vessels, with watertight ramps, indicators showing the position of the bow doors, and banning of undivided decks. What is this ferry?

6) It was a German armed military transport ship that was sunk on 30 January 1945 by Soviet submarine S-13 in the Baltic Sea while evacuating German civilian refugees from East Prussia, Lithuania, Latvia, Poland, and Estonia and military personnel from Gotenhafen (Gdynia) as the Red Army advanced. By one estimate, 9,400 people died, which makes it the largest loss of life in a single ship sinking in history. What is this ship?

7) On 13 January 2012, the Italian cruise ship ran aground, capsized, and later sank in shallow waters after striking an underwater rock off Isola del Giglio, Tuscany, resulting in 32 deaths. The ship was deviated from her planned route at the Isola del Giglio, sailed closer to the island, and struck a rock formation on the seafloor. What is this ship?

8) It was a passenger and cargo steamship built-in 1908 for the Blue Anchor Line to operate between Europe and Australia. In July 1909, on only her second voyage, the ship, en route from Durban to Cape Town, disappeared with 211 passengers and crew aboard. No trace of the ship has ever been found. This ship was referred to as "Australia's Titanic"?

9) Henrik Kurt Carlsen was a Danish-born sea captain who became world-famous in January 1952 when he stayed on his sinking freighter for 13 days. It eventually sank less than 60 kilometers (37 mi) from the safe harbor at Falmouth, Cornwall in England, minutes after the Captain was forced to abandon ship. What is the name of this ship?

10) It was a German battleship of World War II that had a short but spectacular career. it was hit by a torpedo that crippled its steering gear, and the ship was bombarded throughout the night by battleships. On the morning of May 27 King George V and the Rodney, in an hour-long attack, incapacitated the Bismarck, and an hour and a half later it sank after being hit by three torpedoes from the cruiser Dorsetshire. Of some 2,300 crew aboard the Bismarck, only about 110 survived. What is the name of this battleship?

Quiz 27: Mix Quiz 01

Questions

1) Which country has the longest national anthem?

2) What is the tallest statue in the world?

3) What is the world's longest railway and deepest traffic tunnel and the first flat, low-level route through the Alps?

4) Adopted since 1370 Which country uses the oldest flag in the world?

5) This family magazine was first published in 1922 by DeWitt and Lila Wallace and sold exclusively through the mail in the United States. Global editions of this magazine now have a combined circulation of 17 million copies in more than 70 countries, making it the largest paid circulation magazine in the world. What is this magazine?

6) Who were the Indian diplomat and politician elected as the first female president of the United Nations General Assembly?

7) On August 2nd, 1947, a British civilian version of the wartime Lancaster bomber took off from Buenos Aires airport. It was crashed into Mount Tupungato, in the Argentine Andes. An extensive search operation failed to locate the wreckage, despite covering the area of the crash site, and the fate of the aircraft and its occupants remained unknown till late 1990. What is the name of this airplane?

8) The George Cross (GC) is the highest award bestowed by the British government for non-operational gallantry or gallantry, not in the presence of an enemy. What is the only country that was awarded this award in 1942 in recognition of their continuing and heroic struggle against repeated and continuous attacks during World War II?

9) Who is the mathematician who developed logarithms?

10) Having started with a single outlet in Seattle in 1971, this company has expanded to become the largest coffeehouse company in the world – with over 17,000 stores in 50 countries. Interestingly, the company's brand name is derived from the famous American novel Moby Dick by Herman Melville – it is named after the first mate on the whaleship Pequod, commanded by Captain Ahab. What is this famous brand name?

Quiz 28: Mix Quiz 02

Questions

1) Who introduces the postage stamp to the world?

2) Which country in 1893 became the first self-governing nation to extend the right to vote to all adult women?

3) What is the US state which has the same name As a European Country?

4) Planet Uranus has 27 known natural satellites or moons. The five main satellites are named Miranda, Ariel, Umbriel, Titania, and Oberon. The names for these satellites are chosen from characters from the works of William Shakespeare and which English poet?

5) In Japan, What is the well-known term given to the act of committing suicide by cutting open one's belly?

6) The Wall Street Journal is a highly respected financial and business newspaper in the United States that was first published on July 8, 1889. Name the founder of The Wall Street Journal?

7) Amelia Earhart was the first female aviator to fly solo across the Atlantic Ocean. The aircraft flown by Amelia Earhart on her last around-the-world expedition in 1937 was a twin-engine, all-metal monoplane airliner. What was the aircraft's generic name?

8) Who was the first major celebrity to die from an AIDS-related illness?

9) What is the term given to Hitler's the official secret police of Nazi Germany and in German-occupied Europe?

10) In 1999 Climbers of Mount Everest found a body of a British mountaineer who disappeared on the northeast ridge of Everest in 1924. Who is this mountaineer?

Quiz 29:Mix Quiz 03

Questions

1) Who was the first known European explorer to reach the islands of Tasmania, Fiji, and New Zealand?

2) Who were the first climbers confirmed to have reached the summit of Mount Everest?

3) In 1844, a group of 28 weavers and other artisans in a certain English town set up a society to open their store selling food items they could not otherwise afford. Within a decade, over 1,000 cooperative societies appeared across Britain. What is this town, now considered the birthplace of the modern co-op movement?

4) In early June 2012, the social networking and micro-blogging platform Twitter streamlined its bird image logo in an attempt to simplify the 'universally recognizable symbol of Twitter.' According to the company, the new look brings together the Twitter staff's love of ornithology, the need to design within creative constraints, and simple geometry. What is the name of Twitter's iconic logo bird?

5) The world's leading search engine Google is famous for keeping its home page very Spartan with minimum text and features. What name does Google give to the special logos on its home page that is used to celebrate certain holidays, famous anniversaries, and the lives of well-known Persons?

6) What is the world's largest power station in terms of installed capacity?

7) It is generally regarded as the top international honor a mathematician can receive and is sometimes called the equivalent of the Nobel Prize in mathematics. First awarded in 1936, the medal comes with a cash award which at the moment is Canadian Dollars 15,000. By which name is this medal better known?

8) This prize founded in 1979 is awarded to a living architect for his built work; this is often referred to as the Nobel Prize of architecture. What is this prize?

9) Established in 1846 "for the increase and diffusion of knowledge", It is a group of museums and research centers administered by the United States government. Located in Washington DC it comprises nineteen museums, nine research centers, and a zoo many of them historical or architectural landmarks. It is the largest of such complexes in the world. What is this institution which is more or less a museum itself?

10) It is a large game reserve in Narok County, Kenya, named in honor of the ancestral inhabitants of the area and their description of the area. It is globally famous for its exceptional population of lions, leopards, and cheetahs. Name this world-famous reserve?

Quiz 30: Mix Quiz 04

Questions

1) The world's first mobile (or cellular) phone call was made on April 3, 1973, by an American engineer At that time, he was a vice president and division manager at Motorola phone company and led the team that developed the world's first handheld mobile phone who is this engineer, considered the principal inventor of the mobile phone?

2) What is the world's oldest surviving sovereign state in the world which was founded in 301 A.D?

3) Apart from Washington D.C, What is the only other capital city in the world that has been named after a US President?

4) The Organization of the Petroleum Exporting Countries (OPEC) has 13 nations that keep members of this inter-governmental business enterprise set up in 1960. Its founding members are Iran, Iraq, Kuwait. Saudi Arabia and one South American Country. What is this country?

5) The Nobel Prize in Literature is a Swedish literature prize that is awarded annually since 1901. Who was the Swedish author & teacher who became the first woman to win this award in 1909?

6) He was a German physiologist who received the 1901 Nobel Prize in Physiology or Medicine, for his discovery of a diphtheria antitoxin. He was widely known as a "savior of children", as diphtheria used to be a major cause of child death. Name Him?

7) Resulting in 583 fatalities, the Tenerife airport disaster is the deadliest in aviation history. The two Boeing 747 passenger jets, operating KLM Flight 4805 and Pan Am Flight 1736, collided on the runway at Los Rodeos Airport. What is the Spanish archipelago in the Atlantic Ocean where this Airport is situated?

8) Operation Satanic was a bombing operation carried out on 10 July 1985. During the operation, the flagship of the Greenpeace organization was sunk near the Port of Auckland. This was to prevent her from interfering in a French nuclear test in Moruroa atoll in the Pacific. What was the name of this activist ship?

9) Bluetooth is a wireless technology standard for exchanging data over short distances from fixed and mobile devices, and building personal area networks. Name the Sweden-based telecom vendor who invented this technology in 1994?

10) What is the international (or SI) unit for measuring radioactivity?

Answers

Quiz 01: Countries of the World 01

1) The Gambia
2) Lesotho
3) Djibouti
4) Uzbekistan
5) Ecuador & Chile
6) Kazakhstan
7) East Timor
8) Rwanda
9) Mongolia
10) Chile

Quiz 02: Rivers

1) Volga
2) Zambezi
3) Danube
4) Yangtze
5) Mekong
6) Okavango
7) Lena
8) Mackenzie
9) Potomac
10) Murray

Quiz 03: Mix Geography Quiz 01

1) Patagonian Desert
2) Gaza Strip
3) The Pantanal
4) Kaliningrad
5) Saragasso Sea
6) Tibetan Plateau
7) Copacaban
8) Bakassi Peninsula
9) Mariana Trench
10) Siachen Glacier

Quiz 04: Islands

1) Hispaniola
2) Nauru
3) Denmark
4) Martinique
5) Madagascar
6) The Andaman Islands
7) American Samoa
8) Solomon Islands
9) Tierra del Fuego
10) Crete

Quiz 05: Cities and States

1) Quito
2) Uttar Pradesh
3) Andorra la Vella
4) Rhode Island
5) Samarkand
6) Puerto Williams
7) Telangana
8) La Rinconada
9) Bahrain and Qatar
10) Istanbul

Quiz 06: Mountains

1) Alps
2) Mount Narodnaya
3) Ben Nevis
4) Table Mountain
5) Pyrenees
6) Mount Elbrus
7) Sugarloaf Mountain
8) K2
9) Mount Kilimanjaro
10) Nanga Parbat

Quiz 07: Straits and Lakes

1) Strait of Messina
2) Torres Strait
3) Lake Baikal
4) Lake Retba
5) Cook Strait
6) Lake Titicaca
7) Dardanelles
8) Lake Victoria
9) Bab-el-Mandeb
10) Lake Ellsworth

Quiz 08: Mix Geography Quiz 02

1) Goa
2) Andes
3) Chile
4) Italy
5) Belize
6) Port Said and Port Towfik
7) Thar Desert
8) Turks and Caicos Island
9) Borneo
10) Urulu or Ayers Rock

Quiz 09: Countries of the World 02

1) Mali
2) Greece
3) Tanzania
4) Kiribati
5) Monaco
6) Norway
7) Turkmenistan
8) Liberia
9) El Salvador
10) Laos

Quiz:10 Mix Geography Quiz 03

1) Mount Etna
2) Boyoma Falls
3) Honshu
4) Mombasa
5) Durand Line
6) Caucasus Mountains
7) Horseshoe Falls
8) Brazil
9) Sunda Trench
10) Saint Petersburg

Quiz 11:History Quiz 01

1) Augustus Caesar
2) Battle of Poitiers
3) Bactria
4) Constantine the Great
5) Joseon Dynasty
6) Sumerian
7) Montezuma II
8) Genghis Khan
9) The Battle of Okinawa
10) Arthur Wellesley, 1st Duke of Wellington

Quiz 12: Asian Politics 01

1) Rajendra Prasad
2) Albert Einstein
3) Sheikh Mujibur Rahman
4) Sun Yat-sen
5) Jigme Thinley
6) Ramon Magsaysay
7) Liaquat Ali Khan
8) Sukarno
9) Le Duc Tho
10) Sirimavo Bandaranaike

Quiz 13: European Politics 01

1) Robert Walpole
2) Aldo Moro
3) Antonio de Oliveira Salazar
4) William Ewart Gladstone
5) Mikhail Gorbachev
6) Yulia Tymoshenko
7) Golda Meir
8) Makarios III
9) Charles de Gaulle
10) Joseph Goebbels

Quiz 14: African Politics 01

1) Kenneth Kaunda
2) Ahmed ben Bella
3) Elisabeth Domitien
4) Gamal Abdel Nasser
5) Patrice Lumumba
6) Paul Biya
7) Jomo Kenyatta
8) F.W de Klerk
9) Sani Abacha
10) Canaan Banana

Quiz 15: U.S Presidents

1) Theodore Roosevelt
2) William Taft
3) Richard Nixon
4) Franklin Delano Roosevelt
5) Ronald Regan
6) Dwight D. Eisenhower
7) Abraham Lincoln
8) Gerald Ford
9) William Henry Harrison
10) Donald Trump

Quiz 16: History Quiz 02

1) Edward VIII
2) Istanbul
3) Alexander the Great
4) Ivan the Terrible
5) Battle of the Somme
6) Horatio Nelson
7) Enola Gay
8) Battle of Solferino
9) Hammurabi
10) Checkpoint Charlie

Quiz 17: Asian Politics 02

1) Tunku Abdul Rahman
2) Zhou Enlai
3) Ferdinand Marcos
4) Pol Pot
5) David Ben Gurion
6) Eisaku Sato
7) Lee Kwan Yew
8) Jawaharlal Nehru
9) Aung San
10) Hussain Muhammed Ershad

Quiz 18: European Politics 02

1) Nicolae Ceausescu
2) Konrad Adenauer
3) Josip Broz Tito
4) Spencer Perceval
5) Ignacy Jan Paderewski
6) Nikita Khrushchev
7) Slobodan Milosevic
8) William Gladstone
9) Georges Pompidou
10) Walter Ulbricht

Quiz 19: World Politics

1) Anwar el-Sadat
2) Laurent Kabila
3) Joyce Banda
4) Jean-Bedel Bokassa
5) Ellen Johnson Sirleaf
6) Ernesto "Che" Guevara
7) Philadelphia
8) Ralph Bunche
9) Gough Whitlam
10) Operation Barbarosa

Quiz 20:American Politics

1) Fulgencio Batista
2) Spiro Agnew
3) James A Garfield
4) Isabel de Peron
5) Augusto Pinochet
6) Daniel Ortega
7) Kim Campbell
8) Manuel Belgrano
9) Oscar Arias Sanchez
10) Ingrid Betancourt

Quiz 21: Famous People 01

1) Robert Baden-Powell
2) Howard Carter
3) Frederic Auguste Bartholdi
4) Albert John Lutuli
5) Bertrand Piccard & Brian Jones
6) Camille Gutt
7) Martin Luther King, Jr.
8) Dag Carl Hammarskjold
9) Robert Ballard
10) John Hancock

Quiz 22: Successful Entrepreneurs

1) John Pemberton
2) Mukesh Ambani
3) John D Rockefeller
4) Amancio Ortega
5) Jack Dorsey
6) Henry Ford
7) Ralph Lauren
8) Binod Chaudhary
9) Carlos Slim Helu
10) Li Ka-Shing

Quiz 23: Great Women

1) Anna Jarvis
2) Bertha von Suttner
3) Liliane Bettencourt
4) Mata Hari
5) Oprah Winfrey
6) Anne Sullivan Macy
7) Augusta Ada King
8) Virginia Woolf
9) Taslima Nasrin
10) Madeleine Albright

Quiz 24: Famous People 02

1) Louis Bleriot
2) Florence Chadwick
3) Sully Prudhomme
4) Dr. Harold Shipman
5) King Bhumibol Adulyadej (King Rama IX)
6) Admiral Chuichi Nagumo
7) Norman Ernest Borlaug
8) Augusta Ada King, Countess of Lovelace
9) Wangari Maathai
10) Eugene Meyer

Quiz 25: Nobel Laureates

1) Malala Yousafzai
2) Jean-Paul Sartre
3) John B. Goodenough
4) Boris Pasternak
5) Marie Curie
6) Henry Dunant
7) Frederick Sanger
8) Linus Pauling
9) Rabindranath Tagore
10) Lester B. Pearson

Quiz 26: Maritime Disasters

1) RMS Carpathia
2) MV Dona Paz
3) MS Estonia
4) RMS Lusitania
5) MS Herald of Free Enterprise
6) MV Wilhelm Gustloff
7) Costa Concordia
8) SS Waratah
9) Flying Enterprise
10) Bismark

Quiz 27: Mix Quiz 01

1) Greece
2) Statue of Unity
3) Gotthard Base Tunnel
4) Denmark
5) Reader's Digest
6) Vijaya Lakshmi Pandit
7) Stardust
8) Malta
9) John Napier
10) Starbucks

Quiz 28: Mix Quiz 02

1) Roland Hill
2) New Zealand
3) Georgia
4) Alexander Pope
5) Harakiri
6) Charles Henry Dow
7) Lockheed Model 10 Electra
8) Rock Hudson
9) Gestapo
10) George Mallory

Quiz 29: Mix Quiz 03

1) Abel Tasman
2) Edmund Hillary & Tenzing Norgay
3) Rochdale
4) Larry
5) Google Doodles
6) Three Gorges Dam
7) The Fields Medal
8) Pritzker Architecture Prize
9) Smithsonian
10) Maasai Mara National Reserve

Quiz 30: Mix Quiz 04

1) Martin Cooper
2) St Marino
3) Monrovia
4) Venezuela
5) Selma Lagerlöf
6) Emil von Behring
7) Canary islands
8) The Rainbow Warrior
9) Ericsson
10) Becquerel

9 798499 363522